ISBN 0-85116-772-1

DENNIS the MENACE and GNASHER

HAR-HAR! I'M A BUG BUSTER!

GNEE-HEE!

PEST CONTROL LTD

NIGEL PARKINSON

Just then —

THE BUG PHONE!

HELP! BUGS IN MY KITCHEN! 24 MINX ROAD, BEANOTOWN!

So —

LOOK OUT, BUGS! WE'RE ON OUR WAY!

HELP!

OOH!

EEK!

LEAVE THIS TO THE BUG BUSTERS!

GNASH!

HO-HO!

EEK! INTO THE JAR!

PSST! DON'T WORRY, BUGS! I'M ONLY MOVING YOU TO A NEW HOME!

WHEW! WE'LL BE OKAY — IT'S DENNIS!

Soon —

HAR-HAR! YOU'LL LIKE IT HERE!

Suddenly —

CHORTLE! NOW THEY HAVE THE PLACE TO THEMSELVES!

SQUEAL! BUGS!

MUMMY!

HELP!

Later —

BAKERY

A BUG BUSTER! JUST THE PERSON I NEED!

L...LOOK!

OH!

CLEAR THE SHOP — I'LL DEAL WITH IT!

OKAY YOU . . .

SPLODGE

THE NAUGHTIEST, CLEVEREST (ME THINKS) GOBLIN IN BEANOTOWN WOOD

LOOK OUT!

SLAM!

H-HEY!

PEOPLE ARE ALWAYS CHUCKING THEIR RUBBISH INTO OUR WOODS.

IT'S A DISGRACE!

OIL

NO, IT'S NOT — IT'S BRILLIANT!

I'VE GOT A LITTLE WORK TO DO. HEE-HEE!

TAP! TAP!

TOOL KIT

CRASH! BANG! WALLOP!

WH-WHAT'S TH-THAT?

LES PRETEND

LITTLE LARRY

(The rudest brat in Beanotown.)

Humpty Dumpty sat on a chair.
Humpty Dumpty flew up in the air.
Naughty young Larry chuckled
with glee,
"Just what I wanted —
omelette for tea!"

"Mary, Mary, you look scary.
Look at your pimples grow.
Your breath sure smells,
Your stomach swells,
And you've got a hooter
Like a crow!"

"Nursery Crimes"

Sing a song of sickness,
A bucket full of swill,
Four and twenty school kids,
Feeling rather ill.
Frog spawn, worms and maggots,
Tipped in cookie's stew.
Wasn't that a fiendish thing,
for anyone to do?

Hey diddle diddle, a dog did a widdle,
All over Mum's best Persian rug.
A little boy laughed to see such fun,
And gave the dog drinks by the jug.

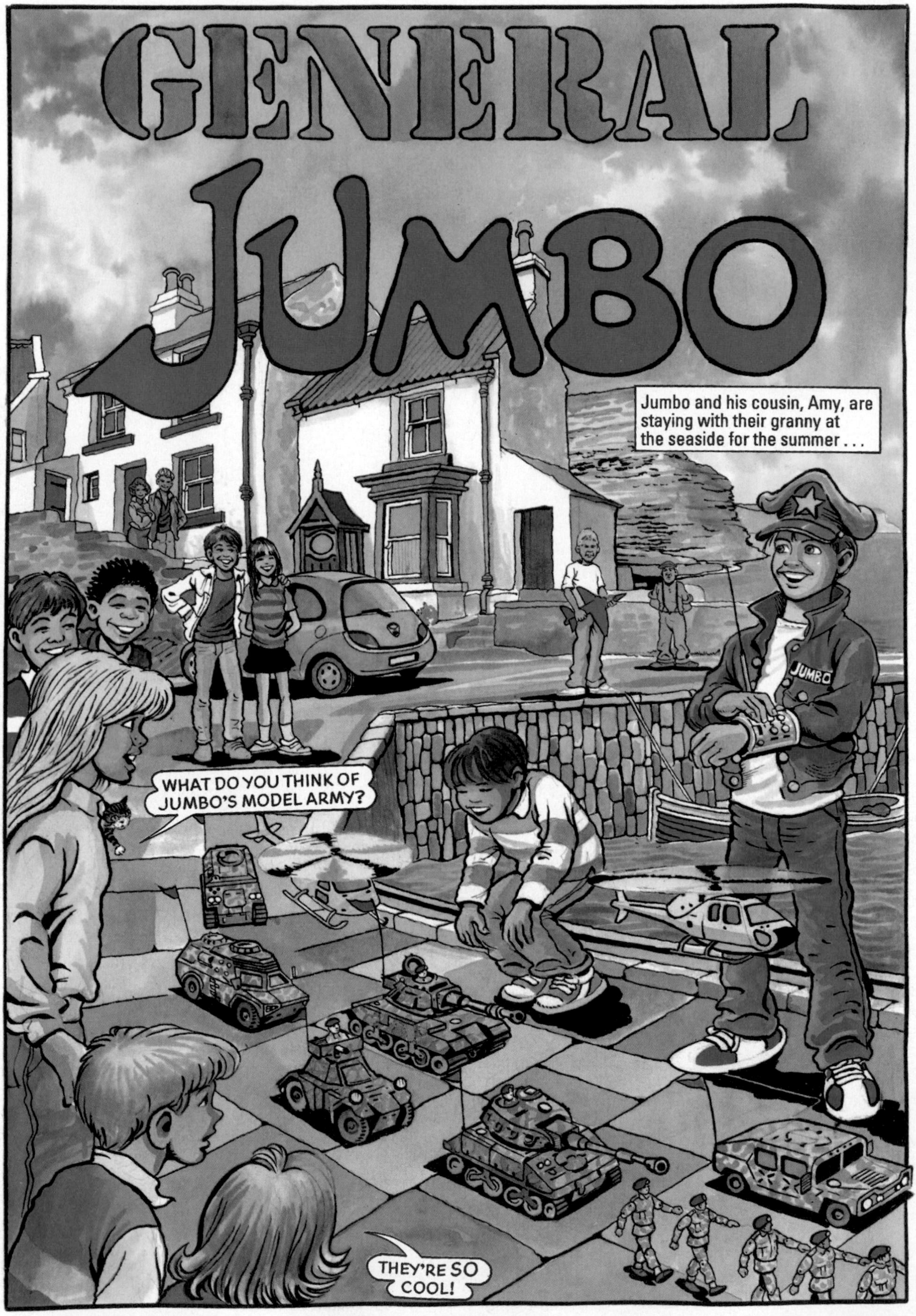
GENERAL
JUMBO
Jumbo and his cousin, Amy, are staying with their granny at the seaside for the summer . . .
JUMBO
WHAT DO YOU THINK OF JUMBO'S MODEL ARMY?
THEY'RE SO COOL!

Back at Gran's —

YOU'LL HAVE TO KEEP OFF THAT FOOT FOR A DAY OR SO. YOU CAN READ YOUR DAD'S OLD BEANO BOOKS.

THE BEANO BOOK
BEANO BOOK
THE BEANO BOOK
THE BEANO BOOK
THE BEANO BOOK

SOMETHING'S GOT TO BE DONE ABOUT THAT RYAN!

I THINK I HAVE AN IDEA. I'LL NEED YOUR HELP . . .

Next morning —

SO! JUMBO'S BACK FOR MORE, IS HE?

SOME PEOPLE JUST NEVER LEARN!

I WONDERED WHEN YOU'D SHOW UP, RYAN!

EH?

MAYBE IT'S YOUR TURN TO LEARN!

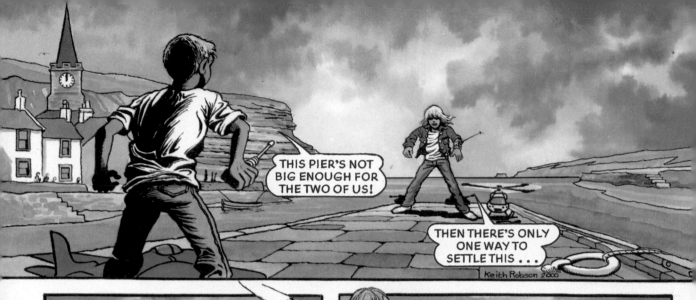

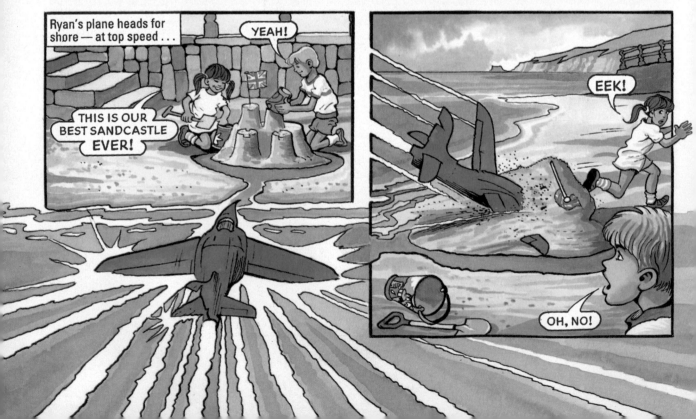

LOOK WHAT YOU'VE DONE TO OUR SANDCASTLE!

MY PLANE'S RUINED!

SERVES YOU RIGHT!

COME ON, RYAN! LET'S HELP THEM BUILD AN EVEN BETTER CASTLE!

YOU MIGHT EVEN FIND THAT IT'S FUN!

So —

COME ON, SLOWCOACH! WE NEED MORE SAND!

HA-HA! I'D LIKE TO SEE YOU DIG FASTER!

THERE! IT'S FINISHED!

YOU SEE? IT'S MUCH MORE FUN WHEN YOU HAVE FRIENDS!

Tea-time —

SO YOU THINK YOUR MINATURE ENGINEERS CAN FIX MY PLANE, JUMBO?

IT'LL BE AS GOOD AS NEW TOMORROW — THEN WE CAN HAVE SOME FUN AT THE BEACH — AS PALS!

MINNIE HA-HA'S

MINNIE CAB

MINNIE MOU...

MINNIE HANDS MAKE LIGHT WORK

NICE BHOY

MINNIE SUBMARINE

MINNIE BUSES

MINNIE APPLE-LASS

BNO...

MINNIE MARKET

MINNIE-STER OF SILLY WALKS

10

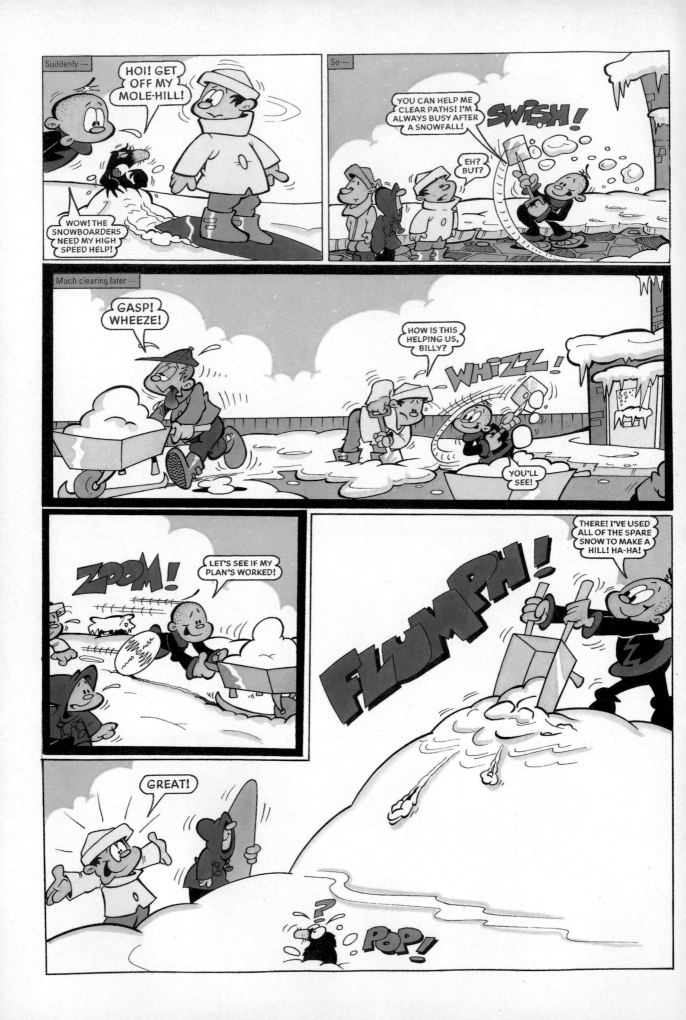

THE BASH STREET KIDS

WHAT ARE YOU DOING, HEADMASTER?

RINGING THE POLICE! A MAJOR CRIME HAS TAKEN PLACE IN THE SCHOOL!

HEAD'S STUDY

OUR BELOVED HEAD

HELLO . . . IT'S THE HEADMASTER HERE. I WANT TO REPORT A TERRIBLE, AWFUL AND DREADFUL THEFT!

OKAY! GIVE ME THE DETAILS AND I'LL SEND SOMEONE AROUND!

WANTED

WANTE

ONE OF MY BELOVED CHOCOLATE DIGESTIVE BISCUITS WAS STOLEN FROM MY STUDY AT PLAYTIME! SOB!

WHAT! WE CAN'T WASTE POLICE TIME LOOKING FOR A MISSING CHOCCY BISCUIT!

OKAY! IS ANYONE GOING TO OWN UP TO NICKING MY JAM DOUGHNUT?

IT WASN'T ME!

AND IT WASN'T HIM, EITHER!

DONK

THUD

IT WASN'T US, HEAD! WE WERE ALL IN THE CLASSROOM DURING PLAYTIME!

YEAH! AND TEACHER HAS AN ALIBI TOO — HE WAS TIED UP AT THE TIME!

HEAD'S STUDY

HOP

HOP

ARE YOU IN THERE, BISCUIT OF MINE?

PROD

IT WASN'T FATTY! WE CAN PROVE THAT!

NOT CHOCOLATE — BLACK DUST! YOU'VE BEEN BITING COAL AGAIN, EH?

OF COURSE! AND IT WAS DELICIOUS! BURP!

RUB!

AND WHERE WERE YOU TWO AT PLAYTIME?

ER... WELL... EM...

SHAKE

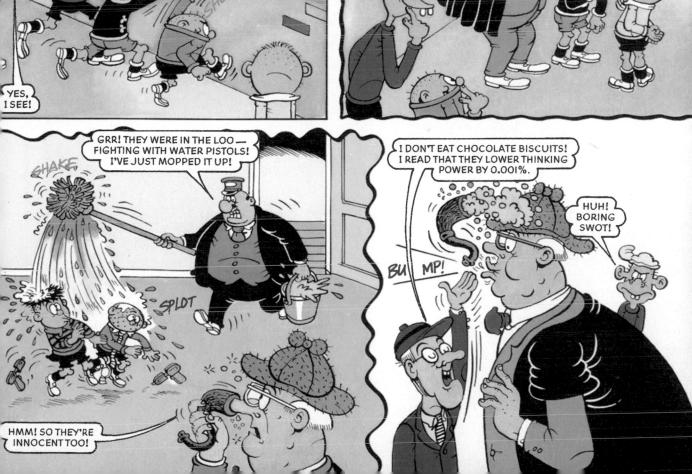

DENNIS THE MENACE in
ROBOT'S REVENGE
REMEMBER LAST YEAR'S BEANO BOOK WHEN WE WENT IN THE MENACECAR TO THE PLANET OF THE BEANOBOTS?
GNESH!
CRACKLE!
FIZZLE!
WE DESTROYED THEM, EH?
FZZUT!
KABOOM!
GNATURALLY!

THE BEARS FACED MANY DANGERS ON THEIR WAY THROUGH THE DESERT...

...THE BURNING SUN WAS HOT ENOUGH TO FRY A MAN'S BRAIN...

IT'S A GOOD JOB PA HASN'T GOT ONE, EH?!

PFFF..!

HMM.?

THERE WERE FEARSOME DESERT LIONS...

ROOAR!

LEAP!

...TREACHEROUS QUICKSANDS...

OH ... BOTHER!

...AND SCAREY RATTLESNAKES!

HISSSSS..?

WHAT WAS THAT HISSING NOISE?

WHAT HISSING NOISE?!

②

WANNABEA...

The UK's SWEETEST SMELLING COMIC
THE BEANO
A DIFFERENT LOOK AT YOUR FAVOURITE COMIC!
TALCUM POWDER
WHUMPH!
SPLISH! SPLASH!
SQUIRT!
Nice Niffy Cologne
AAGH!
COUGH! COUGH!
PRICE 2 PRETTY PANSIES

WALTER
THE SOFTY
AND
FOO-FOO

GOODY GUM DROPS! NOW'S OUR CHANCE FOR FLORAL DISPLAYS, EMBROIDERY AND BALLET!

FAINT!
SWOON!
THUD!
THUMP!

ONE CAN MAKE THE UGLIEST THINGS PRETTY, THANKS TO A FLORAL DISPLAY!

EVEN GNASHER!

EMBROIDERY IS SPIFFING FUN, TOO!

NNNGH! THE SLEEPING BEAUTY IS MY FAVOURITE BALLET! TITTER!

LIFT
PUSH!

IT'LL TAKE A LOT OF WORK, BUT I'LL MAKE DENNIS INTO A BEAUTY!

TWIST
MAKE-UP

OOO! WE'RE LOVING THIS!

SPIN
YIPPITY YAP!
LEAP

Minutes later —

E-HEE! I'VE BORROWED IT SO I CAN BE TOP MINX FOR A CHANGE.

ROWPH! ROWPH!

EEK! BIG BAD BONZO FROM NUMBER TWELEVE.

SNEAKILY DOES IT, MINX FANS.

ZZZ

RAT-A-TAT!

PHTOOM!

ZZZ . . . YEEOW!

AARGH! DOWN, BONZO!

WHAP!

BYE-BYE!

NO DIN-DINS FOR YOU, BONZO. BAD BOY!

HO-HO! MINNIE WOULD BE PROUD OF ME TODAY, MINX FANS.

LES'S DAD
THE OLD
PRETENDER

GOOD! LES IS OUT PRETENDING. NOW'S MY CHANCE.

BACK, WAVES! BACK, I COMMAND YOU.

PUT YOUR HANDS TOGETHER, PLEASE, FOR THE KING . . .

. . . ELVIS PRESLEY — LIVE IN BEANOTOWN!

KARAOKE KING

ME AN' MAH BAND, THE MEMPHIS KARAOKES WOULD LIKE TO DO A LI'L NUMBER FOR Y'ALL.

BLUE, BLUE — BLUE SUEDE SHOES.

WHATEVER YOU DO, LAY OFFA MY BLUE SUEDE . . .

LOOK WHAT I FOUND IN THE POND, DAD.

. . . NYUMPH!

BLUE SUEDE NYUMPH? WEIRD SONG!

RIBBICK! RIBBICK! CROAK!

KARAOKE? CROAKY, MORE LIKE! CHORTLE!

The HEAD-MASTER and OLIVE
SCHOOL COOK

HEAD'S STUDY

AHA! THE HEAD'S HARD AT WORK!

2

Y-ES!

THUD!

FIRE BUNKER

FIRE BUNKER

5

PLOP!

PLONK

PLINK

PLINK

BOUNCE

CRACK!

SUPER! I'M THE MAN! WAHEY!

LET'S GO AND VISIT OLIVE. HEAD'S . . . AHEM . . . BUSY!

KITCHEN

GASP! CAN OLIVE BE IN THERE?

TRA . . . LA . . . LA!

BURBLE

NAUSEOUS NIFF!

MATHS

TOFFEE

GASP! GROO! I CAN SEE WHY NO-ONE LIKES TO WATCH THIS!

PRUNES

CURRY POWDER

RHUBARB

OLD SOCKS

SQUID JELLY

SO YOU BOTH DON'T WORK VERY HARD AT SCHOOL, THEN?

WE NEVER WORK HARD IN THE MORNINGS BECAUSE WE BOTH GO OUT FOR A JOG EVERY AFTERNOON!

After lunch.

HO-HO! YES, A JOG!

TIE!

TIE!

GNASHER'S FLEAS

DODGE CAT

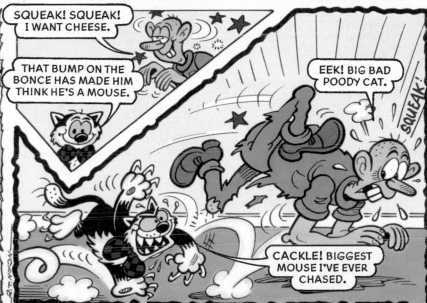

THAT LOT HAVE HAD THEIR CHANCE. WE'LL BE BACK AS TOP STARS IN *the BEANO every week of the year!* SEE YA!

The NUMSKULLS

I WANT FILLED IN!

MY PLEASURE, GNASHER!

GNEE-HEE! THAT TICKLES!

MINNIE THE MINX

HMPH! THIS IS ALL I CAN FIND TO PLAY WITH TODAY.

I SUPPOSE I CAN ALWAYS SPIN ON IT.

SPIN

STEADY ON, MINNIE! UP TO YOUR MINXING TRICKS AGAIN?

DOOPH!

HOWL! THE PAIN! ONLY LOTS OF SWEETIES WILL SOOTHE IT.

LITTLE TWISTER! HERE'S YOUR POCKET MONEY.

GOSH! ANOTHER LITTLE TWISTER. I MUST'VE CAUSED THAT WITH MY SPINNING.

WHIRL

WOW! AND NOW IT'S A BIG TWISTER!

AND IT CAN CHANGE SHAPE, TOO.

SNORT!

NOW THE BULL'S HEADING STRAIGHT FOR THE CHINA SHOP!

CHINA

WHISK

BELLOW!

OLE!

Meanwhile, a tired tradesman is having a nap —

ZZZ

Not a good idea if you're a steeplejack!

TOPPLE

SNORE!

N ZZZ

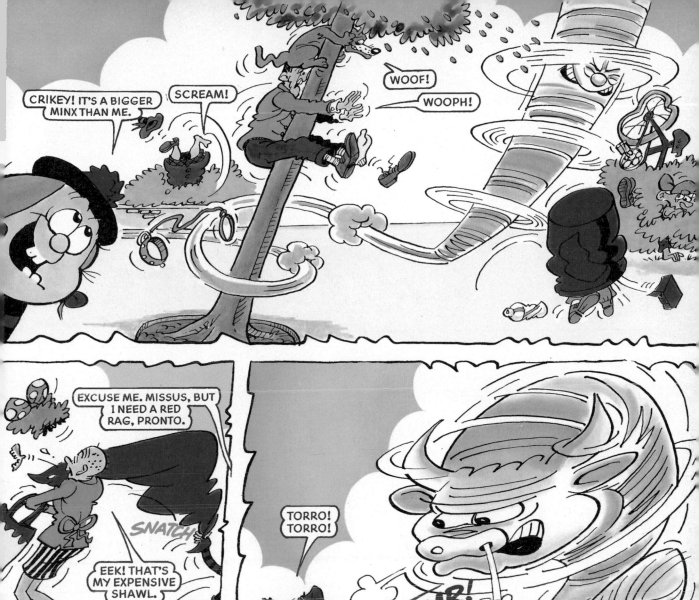

HOW TO BECOME A COLONEL

THANK YOU FOR SHOPPING AT FRESCOS.

AT EASE, YOUNG MAN!

ER, HOW DID YOU BECOME A COLONEL, IF I MAY ASK?

SIMPLE, MY BOY, SIMPLE. CONSTANT PROMOTION THROUGH THE RANKS.

PRICES DOWN

3P OFF

6P OFF

WANT TO HEAR ABOUT MY MILITARY CAREER, DO YOU, LADDIE?

OO! YES, PLEASE!

SECURITY

FRESCOS

FRESCOS

LIKE EVERYONE ELSE, I STARTED OUT AS A PRIVATE.

'EFT!
'IGHT!

TUG!

TRAMP!
TRAMP!

CLEVER ME THOUGHT OF A WAY TO CLEAN ALL OF THE TOILETS AT THE SAME TIME.

A QUICK BLAST OF WATER AND . . .

OO!

CLICK!

CLICK

TOILETS

CLICK

I WAS QUICKLY MADE A MAJOR. LUCKILY MUMMY HAD ALREADY MADE ME THE UNIFORM.

SECURITY

SUITS ME, EH?

TUG!

TUG!

SO SMART!

SPIN

TWIRL

SPIN

I WAS CLEARLY UNSUITED TO THE LOWER RANKS, SO I WAS SWIFTLY MADE A COLONEL.

PIN!

AND SO, IN THE GREAT TRADITION OF THE BRITISH ARMY I WAS PROMOTED ALL THE WAY UP TO THE RANK OF COLONEL.

AMAZING!

FRESCOS

FRESC

CLICK!

Your History

· Picasso ·

THE **BASH STREET KIDS**

W ... WHAT'S GOING ON?

WHEEZE!

PUFF! PANT!

EH?

DUST!

DUST!

EH? MOST ODD!

CLASS II B

DO NOT DISTURB

CLASS II B

WOW! WHAT'S THIS?

BREAKFAST TIME!

YAWN!

NIFF

YAWN!

YAWN!

WHERE'S TEACHER?

HE'S NOT PULLING HIS WEIGHT IN THIS HOTEL!

I'LL CALL HIM!

DING! DING! DING!

CARRY THE BAGS OUT, BOY!

HO-HO-HO!

HUMPH! YES, SIR!

NOT SO MUCH PULLING HIS WEIGHT — MORE CARRYING IT! HA-HA!

THANKS FOR YOUR HELP, BOY!

TOSS!

TOSS!

GASP! PUFF! WHEEZE!

AHEM! WE'LL KEEP THESE TIPS FOR THE BELL BOY! HE HASN'T GOT ANY HANDS FREE AT THE MOMENT! CHUCKLE!

BALL BOY

HEY, TEAM-MATES. EVER NOTICED HOW FOOTBALL TEAMS HAVE SCAREY NICK-NAMES?

SUCH AS BALL BOY?

MILLWALL, FOR EXAMPLE.

MILLWALL? WHAT'S THEIR NICK-NAME?

THE LIONS!

YIKES! DON'T LET THEM EAT US!

WAAH!

BUT THE SCARIEST NICK-NAME OF ALL BELONGS TO BLACKPOOL.

BLACKPOOL? WHAT'S THEIR NICK-NAME? NO, DON'T TELL US! WE'RE AFRAID.

THEY'RE KNOWN AS THE SEA-SIDERS!

THE SEA-SIDERS? THAT'S NOT A SCAREY NICK-NAME!

NO IN THE LEAST!

ASHAMED!

DIP!

IT IS! IT REMINDS ME OF THE SEA-SIDE HOLIDAY I HAD WITH MY MUM AND DAD! OO! THE SHAME!

HOW AWFUL!

APPALLING!

HORRIFIC!

BEA-GINNINGS

LOOK, BEA! WE'VE BOUGHT YOU A LOVELY NEW BATH!

HAVE A BATH BEFORE BEDDY-TIME!

YUK! ME WOULDN'T BE SEEN WET IN IT!

GET IN THERE!

I'LL JUST GET A SPONGE.

S'ALRIGHT, ME CAN REACH 'AT BRUSH.

EEK! DIRTY! DIRTY! THAT'S A TOILET BRUSH!

WHAT ELSE DO YOU HAVE IN THERE?

EM, SCALES.